THE Food Hygiene HANDBOOK

Richard A. Sprenger
B.Sc. (Hons.), D.M.S., F.C.I.E.H., F.S.O.F.H.T., M.R.E.H.I.S.
Managing Director, Highfield.co.uk Ltd

First published 1982
Republished 1985/86/87/89/91/92/93/95/97/99/00/01/02
16th Edition 2003

"Vue Pointe", Spinney Hill, Sprotbrough, Doncaster, South Yorkshire, DN5 7LY, U.K.
Tel: +44 (0)1302 391999 Fax: +44 (0)1302 783303
E-mail: jayne@foodhygiene.tv
ISBN 1 904544 06 1

www.highfield.co.uk

www.foodsafetytrainers.co.uk

Printed by Apple Tree Print Tel: 01302 314011

Highfield .co.uk limited

Improving Food Safety

CONTENTS

Key questions

Introduction

Every year millions of people in the U.K. suffer from diarrhoea, vomiting and stomach cramps. Many of these people will have eaten contaminated or poisonous food and a few of them will die. Those most at risk include the very young, the frail elderly, persons who are already ill or convalescing, persons with allergies to specific foods and even pregnant women.

Food Poisoning Trends in England and Wales

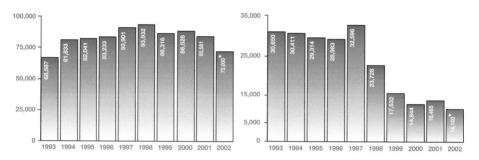

NOTIFICATIONS OF FOOD POISONING (1993-2002)
(includes many cases of diarrhoea/vomiting that are not foodborne)

SALMONELLA IN HUMANS (1993-2002)

Courtesy of P.H.L.S. Communicable Disease Surveillance Centre
*Provisional

THE TEN MAIN FAULTS CONTRIBUTING TO FOOD POISONING OUTBREAKS

1 Food prepared too far in advance and stored at room temperature, i.e. not under refrigeration
2 Cooling food too slowly prior to refrigeration
3 Not reheating food to high enough temperatures to destroy food poisoning bacteria
4 The use of cooked food contaminated with food poisoning bacteria
5 Undercooking
6 Not thawing frozen poultry for sufficient time
7 Cross-contamination from raw food to high-risk food
8 The consumption of raw food such as shellfish, eggs or milk
9 Storing hot food below 63°C
10 Infected food handlers

The number of salmonella isolations and general outbreaks have fallen over the last ten years. However, the notifications of food poisoning and suspected food poisoning have remained at an unacceptable level despite increased training and improved hygiene standards. Possible reasons include:

1 increases in the number of foodborne pathogens in and on raw foods, such as meat, eggs, shellfish, vegetables and fruit (intensive farming and the reduction in the number of slaughterhouses);

2 better awareness of the public due to greater publicity and food hygiene training;

3 increased amounts of 'exotic' imported foods;

4 more holidays abroad;

5 increase of meals consumed outside the home;

6 improved investigation and detection;

7 discovery of new pathogens;

8 increasing numbers of susceptible people, especially the elderly;

9 reduction in the use of preservatives;

10 changes in preparation and cooking methods in the home, e.g. more ready-prepared food and the incorrect use of microwave ovens.

Although the ten most common faults contributing to food poisoning are listed on page 3, the most important reasons are negligence, ignorance, poor management and a failure to implement good hygiene practices. Food poisoning can be prevented by effective supervision, instruction and training of food handlers by knowledgeable managers. Staff must be aware of the specific hazards associated with their activities and how these hazards may be controlled. A hazard is the potential to cause harm to the consumer and the main hazards are:

1 the contamination of food by bacteria, poisonous chemicals or foreign bodies, such as glass, nails or insects;

2 multiplication of bacteria to levels which could cause food poisoning because of storage at the wrong temperature;

3 the survival of food poisoning bacteria because of inadequate cooking/processing.

Bacterial hazards

Chemical hazards and foreign bodies

This book provides you with the necessary information to control these hazards and if you apply this knowledge in your food business you should not be responsible for causing a food poisoning outbreak.

Furthermore, if you can answer all of the questions at the end of each section, you will be well on the way to passing any of the Foundation food hygiene course examinations.

After reading this book you should:

1	know the causes of food poisoning;
2	know how to prevent food poisoning and food complaints;
3	know how to identify and control hazards involved in the purchase, storage, preparation, cooking and serving of food;
4	know how to monitor controls and take corrective action;
5	understand stock rotation, food spoilage and preservation;
6	know how to use refrigerators and freezers correctly;
7	be aware of the standards of personal hygiene required by food handlers;
8	understand the importance of effective design and construction of food premises and equipment;
9	know how to dispose of waste safely and properly;
10	know the common pests found in food premises and how they can be controlled;
11	understand the correct cleaning procedures;
12	understand how food legislation affects a food business.

Food hygiene

Understanding food hygiene

Food hygiene is more than cleanliness; it includes all practices involved in:

1. protecting food from risk of contamination, including harmful bacteria, poisons and foreign bodies;
2. preventing any bacteria present multiplying to an extent which would result in the illness of consumers or the early spoilage of the food;
3. destroying any harmful bacteria in the food by thorough cooking or processing;
4. discarding unfit or contaminated food.

The cost of poor food hygiene:

1. food poisoning outbreaks and sometimes death;
2. food contamination and customer complaints;
3. pest infestations;
4. waste food due to spoilage;
5. the closure of food premises by local authority action;
6. fines and costs of legal action taken because of contraventions in hygiene legislation, or because of the sale of unfit or unsatisfactory food;
7. civil action taken by food poisoning sufferers;
8. loss of production and food which has to be destroyed;
9. decontamination cleaning and replacement of damaged equipment.

Poor hygiene can result in food complaints, illness and fines

All of these factors will contribute to a lowering of profits. If the commercial viability of the premises is threatened, employees may lose overtime, bonuses or even their jobs. It is therefore in the best interests of everyone involved in the preparation and handling of food to observe the highest standards of food hygiene.

The benefits of good food hygiene:

1. satisfied customers, a good reputation and increased business;
2. compliance with food safety legislation;
3. less food wastage and increased shelf-life of food;
4. good working conditions, higher staff morale and lower staff turnover, which promote increased productivity.

All of these factors will contribute to higher profits.

Bacteria

Bacteria are microscopic organisms, often referred to as germs, which are found everywhere, including on and in man, on food, in water, soil and air.

Most bacteria are harmless and some are essential, for example, for breaking down decaying matter, or for food manufacture, such as cheese and yoghurt. However, a small number of bacteria cause food spoilage and some, known as pathogens, are responsible for causing illness. Food poisoning bacteria produce toxins (poisons) either in the food or inside the body.

The number of bacteria present in food may be used to determine whether or not the food has been handled correctly. (Usually checked in a laboratory.)

Bacteria exist everywhere

It is impracticable to operate a food business without food poisoning bacteria being present at one time or another. It is therefore essential that they are denied the opportunity to contaminate high-risk food and denied the conditions which allow them to multiply to a level where they present a risk to customers.

Requirements for bacterial growth

Bacteria responsible for causing food poisoning need the following conditions to enable them to grow and, in some cases, produce toxins.

Warmth

The best temperature for the growth of most food poisoning bacteria is around 37°C (body temperature), although they can grow quite quickly between 20°C and 50°C. To prevent their growth we must ensure that the temperature of food is kept below 5°C or above 63°C. The temperature range of 5°C to 63°C is often referred to as the **'danger zone'**.

Food poisoning bacteria reproduce rapidly in warm food rooms, but most will not grow in a refrigerator (1°C to 4°C) and none in frozen food (-18°C), although many will survive and start multiplying when the food thaws.

Some bacteria are able to produce spores, which protect them against adverse conditions such as high temperatures, drying and disinfection. Spores are a resting phase and they do not multiply. When favourable conditions return the spore releases the bacterium, which can then start to grow and multiply. This process is known as germination.

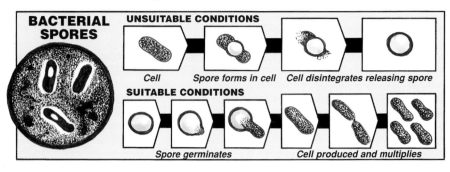

BACTERIAL SPORES

UNSUITABLE CONDITIONS

Cell   Spore forms in cell   Cell disintegrates releasing spore

SUITABLE CONDITIONS

Spore germinates   Cell produced and multiplies

Food and moisture

High protein foods are preferred by bacteria, especially meat, poultry and dairy produce. Foods such as dried egg, gravy or milk powder do not provide the conditions necessary for growth. However, once water or milk is added to the powder, any bacteria present will start growing. It is essential, therefore, to use such food as soon as possible after adding liquid.

Other foods, which do not support bacterial growth, include those containing high concentrations of sugar, salt, acid or other preservatives.

Requirements for bacterial growth

WARMTH

TIME

FOOD/MOISTURE

8

Time

Given the right conditions of food, moisture and warmth, some bacteria can divide into two every ten minutes. This process is known as binary fission. If there is sufficient time, a few bacteria can multiply to such an extent that there is enough present to cause food poisoning. For this reason it is essential that high-risk foods are not left in the **danger zone for longer than is absolutely necessary.**

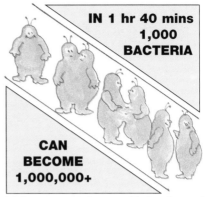

IN 1 hr 40 mins
1,000
BACTERIA

CAN
BECOME
1,000,000+

High-risk foods

High-risk foods are ready-to-eat foods, which support the multiplication of harmful bacteria and are intended for consumption without treatment, such as cooking, which would destroy such organisms. These foods are usually proteins, they must be protected from contamination and require refrigerated storage. They must be kept separate from raw foods. Examples include:

1. cooked meat and cooked poultry;
2. cooked meat products including pâtés, spreads, gravy, stews, meat pies and stock;
3. milk, cream, artificial cream, custards and dairy produce;
4. eggs and products made from raw eggs, e.g. mayonnaise, mousses, hollandaise sauce and quiches;
5. shellfish and other seafoods including oysters, prawns and crabs;
6. cooked rice.

All of the above are frequently implicated in outbreaks of food poisoning, especially cooked poultry, raw egg products and cooked meat. Unfortunately, contaminated food usually looks, tastes and smells completely normal and is unlikely to be detected without laboratory examination.

What are bacteria, toxins and spores?
Where are food poisoning bacteria found?
What types of bacteria cause problems for the food industry?
What are the requirements for bacterial growth?
What are high-risk foods?

Food poisoning and foodborne diseases

Food poisoning

Food poisoning is an acute illness, which usually occurs within one to 36 hours of eating contaminated or poisonous food. Symptoms normally last from one to seven days and include one or more of the following: abdominal pain, diarrhoea, vomiting, nausea and fever. (Allergies are not food poisoning.)

Food poisoning may be caused by:

1. bacteria or their toxins;
2. moulds(mycotoxins);
3. chemicals such as insecticides, cleaning agents and weedkillers;
4. metals such as lead, copper and mercury;
5. poisonous plants such as deadly nightshade and toadstools.
6. poisonous fish or shellfish

Bacterial food poisoning is by far the commonest and in some instances may result in death. A large number of bacteria are usually involved and this normally requires them to multiply within the food.

IMPORTANT FOOD POISONING BACTERIA

Bacteria	Source	Onset period	Typical symptoms and duration of illness
Salmonella	Raw meat, raw milk, raw eggs, raw poultry, carriers, pets, rodents, terrapins, flies, sewage/water	usually 12 to 36 hours	Abdominal pain, diarrhoea, vomiting and fever (1 to 7 days)
Clostridium perfringens	Animal and human excreta, soil (on vegetables), dust, insects and raw meat	usually 12 to 18 hours	Abdominal pain and diarrhoea. Vomiting is rare (12 to 48 hours)
Staphylococcus aureus	Human nose, mouth, skin, boils and cuts. Raw milk from cows or goats	1 to 7 hours	Abdominal pain, mainly vomiting, some diarrhoea, prostration and subnormal temperatures (6 to 24 hours)
Clostridium botulinum	Soil, fish, meat and vegetables	usually 12 to 36 hours	Difficulties in swallowing, talking and breathing, double vision and paralysis of the cranial nerves. Fatalities are common and the recovery of survivors may take several months
Bacillus cereus (i) Toxin in food	Cereals, especially rice, dust and soil	1 to 5 hours	Vomiting, abdominal pain and some diarrhoea (12 to 24 hours)
(ii) Toxin in intestine	As above	8 to 16 hours	Abdominal pain, diarrhoea and some vomiting (1 to 2 days)

Sources of Salmonella

Sources of Staphylococcus aureus

Sources of Clostridium perfringens

Moulds(mycotoxins)

Moulds are often responsible for the spoilage of food, especially baked products and fruit, due to prolonged, unsatisfactory storage. However, some moulds produce mycotoxins which cause illness and sometimes death. Foods involved include nuts, figs and apple juice.

Chemical food poisoning

Acute food poisoning from chemicals is rare and usually results, accidentally, from poisonous chemicals being stored in unlabelled food containers, contamination of food by significant amounts of chemical (insecticides or cleaning agents) or excessive amounts of chemical additives.

Metallic food poisoning

Acute metallic food poisoning is also quite rare and usually results from acid food or drink being in contact with certain metals such as copper, cadmium or zinc. Symptoms, mainly vomiting and abdominal pain, usually develop within an hour.

Poisonous plants/fish

Poisonous plants rarely cause food poisoning in commercial premises. However, cases of poisoning from toadstools, tea contaminated with deadly nightshade, undercooked red kidney beans and the Japanese puffer fish have been recorded.

"As I thought! Definitely metallic food poisoning"

Foodborne diseases

Other illnesses, which can be transmitted via food, include typhoid, paratyphoid, tuberculosis, dysentery, hepatitis A (virus) and brucellosis. However, unlike most cases of food poisoning, only small numbers of organisms are required to cause the illness and a multiplication of organisms within the food is not necessary.

The bacteria and viruses responsible are found, among other places, in man's intestines and the chain of infection is the same as that involved in food poisoning, i.e: the faecal-oral route

Three types of bacteria causing foodborne disease are of particular note.

Campylobacter which is responsible for more cases of illness than salmonella and is found in raw poultry, raw meat, raw milk, farm animals, pets, sewage and birds. The onset period is two to five days and symptoms include fever, diarrhoea (often bloody), colicky abdominal pain and nausea.

Listeria which is able to multiply below 3°C, albeit very slowly and is widely distributed in the environment including animal and human carriers, sewage and raw milk. The onset period is one to 70 days and 'flu like' symptoms include fever and diarrhoea. (There is a risk of abortion in pregnant women.)

E. coli O157 which may result in kidney failure in children and often results in fatalities of elderly persons. It is found in the intestine of cattle, sheep and humans, sewage, meat and raw milk. The onset period is usually three to four days and symptoms include nausea, diarrhoea (often bloody) and severe abdominal cramps.

Viral gastroenteritis

A large number of reported cases of diarrhoea and vomiting result from infection with viruses. Viruses are much smaller than bacteria and do not multiply in food. The vast majority of cases result from airborne infection or person to person spread by the faecal oral route, as only a small number of viral particles are needed to cause infection. Noroviruses are the major cause of viral foodborne illness. The onset period is around 15 to 60 hours and symptoms include vomiting (projectile) , some diarrhoea, abdominal pain, fever and nausea. The illness is usually short, lasting around 24 hours.

Sewage contamination of food can result in foodborne illness

What is food poisoning?
What are the sources, causes and symptoms of food poisoning?
Which foodborne disease organism multiplies under refrigeration?
What is the difference between food poisoning and foodborne disease?
Which food poisoning organism affects the nervous system?
State four sources of salmonella
Which types of food poisoning have the shortest incubation periods?

The prevention of food poisoning

Food poisoning rarely occurs because of a single isolated mistake. Food poisoning results from management failing to identify hazards and/or failing to control these hazards. The food poisoning chain consists of three major hazards:

1. the contamination of high-risk food;
2. the multiplication of bacteria within the food;
3. the survival of bacteria within the food.

Controlling these hazards breaks the chain and prevents food poisoning.

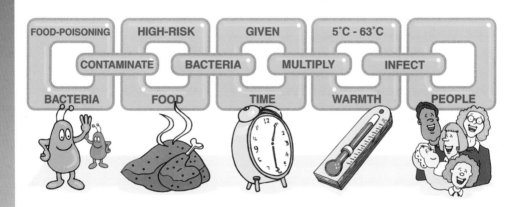

FOOD-POISONING   HIGH-RISK   GIVEN   5°C - 63°C

CONTAMINATE   BACTERIA   MULTIPLY   INFECT

BACTERIA   FOOD   TIME   WARMTH   PEOPLE

Protect food from contamination by:

1. purchasing food from reputable suppliers;
2. effective instruction, supervision and training of food handlers;
3. a high standard of personal hygiene and good hygiene practices (keep food covered and minimise handling) and the provision of adequate, suitable facilities for securing personal hygiene;
4. well-designed and constructed food premises and food rooms;
5. effective pest control;

Avoid handling food

14

6   the separation of raw and high-risk food at all stages of delivery, storage, preparation, serving and distribution. Particular care is needed when thawing raw poultry and cooling cooked meat;

7   effective storage and disposal of waste and unfit food;

8   well-designed and proper use of suitable equipment/utensils;

9   effective cleaning and disinfection. Particular care is needed with wiping cloths.

Prevent bacteria within food from multiplying by:

1   storing food out of the danger zone. Food should be kept below 5°C, e.g. in a refrigerator or kept above 63°C, e.g. in a bain marie;

2   ensuring that during preparation, food is within the danger zone for as short a time as possible. High-risk food must not be left in the ambient temperatures of kitchens or serving areas, unless in the course of preparation or needed for immediate consumption;

3   cooling food as rapidly as possible;

4   not allowing dried foods to absorb moisture.

5   using suitable preservatives such as salt, sugar or vinegar (acid);

6   fermentation e.g. in the making of salami or yoghurt.

N.B. Preservatives and fermentation also assist in destroying harmful bacteria.

Destroy those bacteria within food by:

1   thorough cooking;

2   heat processing such as pasteurisation, sterilisation or canning;

A combination of a suitable temperature and sufficient time is always required to destroy bacteria. The time and temperature required will depend on the particular organism. For example, spores of *Clostridium perfringens* are much more heat resistant than salmonella bacteria. Some spores can survive boiling for up to five hours.

Pasteurisation of milk can be as low as 63°C for 30 minutes, whereas the canning of vegetables requires a minimum of 121°C for three minutes. Cooking temperatures of at least 75°C should normally be achieved at the centre of food to ensure safety. Foods such as stews should be cooked at temperatures approaching 100°C.

How can the contamination of high-risk food be prevented?
How can bacteria in food be destroyed?
How can temperature be used to prevent food poisoning?

Contamination hazards

Contamination is the occurrence of any objectionable or harmful matter in the food or the food environment. Food may be contaminated before delivery to a business or it may become contaminated as a result of poor hygiene practices.

There are three types of contamination of high-risk food.

Microbial contamination
(bacteria, viruses, moulds, yeasts and parasites):

1 bacterial contamination which usually occurs within food premises because of ignorance, inadequate space, poor design or because of food handlers taking short cuts;

2 viral contamination occurs from an infected person or involves raw food such as oysters grown in sewage-contaminated water;

3 parasites which may be present in the raw meat or fish. (They develop in the live animal or fish);

4 moulds and yeasts which are primarily responsible for spoilage.

Microbial contamination is usually the most serious and may result in food spoilage, food poisoning or even death.

Physical contamination by foreign bodies which may be dangerous, e.g. glass or nails, but is normally unpleasant and a nuisance.

Chemical contamination from pesticides, excess additives or industrial/cleaning chemicals.

Food should never be stored near poisonous chemicals, and such chemicals should never be stored in empty food containers.

Sources of food poisoning bacteria

The person: People commonly harbour food poisoning bacteria in the nose, mouth, intestine, cuts and also on the skin. Food may be contaminated directly by the hands, sneezing or coughing, or indirectly by sewage-contaminated water. All water used in food premises should be suitably treated, e.g. by chlorination. The Aberdeen typhoid outbreak was due to cans of Argentinian corned beef, which had been cooled in sewage-polluted water.

Raw food: Raw food is particularly hazardous, especially red meat, poultry (a significant percentage of frozen and fresh birds may carry *salmonella*), untreated milk, eggs and shellfish such as oysters. Raw food should always be kept separate from high-risk food. The liquid from thawing foods, especially frozen poultry, must not be allowed to contaminate wiping cloths, high-risk food or equipment used for high-risk food.

Soil harbours harmful bacteria, and care must be taken when bringing vegetables into food rooms.

Insects: Several insects may transmit food poisoning bacteria to food. Flies and cockroaches present the greatest hazard because of their feeding habits and the sites which they visit. Flies often land on animal faeces where they pick up large numbers of bacteria on their hairy bodies. In addition, they defecate and vomit previous meals back onto the food as they feed.

Careless use of insecticide may result in dead insects ending up in food.

Cockroaches often live in sewers and commonly feed on infected waste. They hide in the most inaccessible places in food rooms and may transfer food poisoning organisms from their legs and bodies to food and equipment on which they walk.

Rodents: Both rats and mice commonly excrete organisms such as salmonellae. Contamination of food may occur from droppings, urine, hairs and gnawing. Food-contact surfaces on which rodents have walked must be disinfected before use. Food suspected of being contaminated by rodents must be destroyed.

Dust: There are always large numbers of bacteria in dust and floating about in the air. Open food should always be covered when cleaning is carried out, especially dusting and sweeping.

Refuse and waste food: Waste and unfit food must not be allowed to accumulate in food rooms. Care must be taken to avoid contamination of food from waste either directly or indirectly. Food operatives must wash their hands after handling refuse. Refuse receptacles are a favourite breeding place for flies and must always have tight-fitting lids, which are replaced after use.

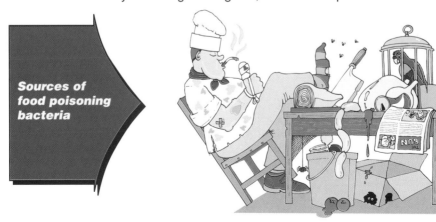

Sources of food poisoning bacteria

Animals and birds: Both domestic and wild animals are known to carry harmful bacteria on their bodies and in their intestines. Furthermore, dirt can be transferred to food from their feet, and hairs and feathers may end up in the food. Pets must always be kept out of food rooms. Terrapins are occasionally implicated in cases of food poisoning through contact with infected water. Other incidents have occurred because of contamination of food by bird droppings.

Vehicles and routes of bacterial contamination

Sometimes, harmful bacteria pass directly from the source to high-risk food, but, as bacteria are usually static and the sources may not be in direct contact with food, the bacteria rely on other things to transfer them to food. These things are known as vehicles and the main ones are:

1 hands; **2** cloths and equipment;
3 hand-contact surfaces; **4** food-contact surfaces.

Cross-contamination is the transfer of the bacteria from contaminated (usually raw) foods to high-risk foods and may be:

1 **direct** when, for example, raw meat touches cooked meat;

2 **by drip**, for example, blood dripping from raw meat stored above cooked meat; or

3 **indirect**, for example, when a food handler prepares cooked meat after handling raw meat without washing their hands or when the same surface is used for both raw food and high-risk food without cleaning and disinfecting between uses. Indirect contamination using an intermediate vehicle is by far the commonest.

SOURCES, VEHICLES AND ROUTES OF CONTAMINATION

Sources *Vehicles* *High-risk food*

Physical and chemical contaminants

Foreign bodies and chemicals found in food may be brought into food premises with the raw materials or introduced during storage, preparation, service or display. If not controlled and/or removed they are likely to result in a customer complaint. Sources include:

Raw ingredients e.g. stones, glass, pests, wood, metal, bones, dirt, cigarette ends, natural poisons, vegetable stalks, flaking paint, grease and oil;

Buildings/equipment e.g. wood, condensation, flaking paint/rust, glass, grease, oil, screws, nuts and bolts;

Notice boards e.g. paper and drawing pins;

Packaging materials e.g. cardboard, paper, string, staples, wood, plastic and polythene;

Maintenance operatives e.g. swarf, screws, nuts, bolts, wire, fibres and cloth;

Food handlers/visitors e.g. jewellery, fingernails, hair, buttons, pen tops, soiled bandages, plasters, cigarette ends, fibres and cloth, buttons and hair;

Cleaning materials/equipment e.g. bristles, bits of cloth and paper;

Pests e.g. bodies, droppings, webbing, larvae/eggs and feathers;

Pesticides e.g. spraying on food/equipment, rodent bait above open food and contaminated raw materials;

Additives e.g. excess nitrates or sulphur dioxide;

Chemicals e.g. detergents, disinfectants, oil and grease

Industrial chemicals e.g. freezer refrigerants, veterinary drugs and fertilisers;

Environmental contaminants e.g. dioxins;

Sabotage e.g. needles, razor blades, toothpicks and glass.

Although there are many different types of foreign bodies, it is essential that managers are aware of those commonly found in their particular sector of the food industry and that they exercise all due diligence to secure their removal or prevent their introduction. Food handlers must observe all company rules and take appropriate precautions to ensure that they are not responsible for the contamination of food.

What is food contamination and what types exist? What are the sources, vehicles and routes of contamination? List examples of physical contaminants

Purchase, storage, temperature control, preparation, cooking and serving of food

The purchase, receipt and storage of food

Choosing a supplier
It is essential to purchase food from reputable suppliers who have demonstrated a commitment to high standards of food hygiene. If contaminated high-risk food is delivered it will be difficult to detect.

Controls to minimise hazards from supplies/suppliers
Select the least hazardous materials/ingredients, e.g. pasteurised egg and ready prepared vegetables.

Only use reputable suppliers. Specify the standard and quality of product required including the delivery temperature.

Receipt of raw materials
The main hazards associated with food deliveries are contaminated food and the multiplication of bacteria as a result of prolonged delays after unloading and before refrigeration. Unsatisfactory delivery vehicles or drivers may indicate unsatisfactory deliveries.

Controls
All food should be inspected before placing in storage. Deliveries should be checked for freshness, temperature, colour, odour, contamination, infestations and satisfactory packaging and labelling. Contaminated food from unapproved sources, high-risk food above 8°C, frozen food above -15°C, food with evidence of pest activity, food which is not covered or in damaged packaging or which is out of date is suspect and may need to be rejected. The supervisor should usually be notified.

As far as practicable, external packaging should not be brought into food preparation areas. A separate deboxing area is recommended. Unloading should be completed as quickly as possible. Staff should be trained to deal with deliveries effectively and to prevent contamination occurring.

Food storage
Correct storage is fundamental to the hygienic operation of any food business. Failure to ensure satisfactory storage conditions will result in hazards (contamination and multiplication of bacteria), mould, spoilt food, discolouration, staleness and pest infestation.

Storage conditions should ensure that the nutritional value, appearance, taste and fitness of food are of the highest standard. Storage areas must not be overloaded and the available space must be taken into account when purchasing food.

Dry-food stores
Rooms used for the storage of dried and canned foods should be suitable for

this purpose, vermin-proof and kept clean and tidy. Hazards encountered include soiled delivery trays, pest infestations, damaged and leaking cartons, rusty cans, out-of-date stock, soil from root vegetables and chemical contamination.

Controls

Keep stores dry, cool, well lit and well ventilated. Effective pest control measures, storage of food at least 15cm above the floor and stock rotation systems are essential. Care with deboxing/opening sacks will avoid foreign body contamination. Food should be stored away from the walls and pipes affected by condensation and on suitable shelves such as tubular stainless steel racks, or in mobile rodent-proof bins. Spillages should be cleared away promptly. If possible, fruit and vegetables should be stored separately from other food. Fruit should be examined regularly as mould spreads rapidly. Vegetables heavily contaminated with soil should be stored below, for example, fruit or lettuce on the vegetable rack. Alternatively, ready-prepared vegetables should be used. Potatoes should be stored in the dark to prevent sprouting or turning green. A separate store should be used for storing cleaning chemicals.

Staff should be trained to store food correctly, to remove spillages, how to rotate stock and to recognise signs of pests and unfit food.

Canned foods

The risk from canned foods is very small compared with the number produced and this safety record will continue if:

1 blown cans are not used;

2 badly-dented, seam-damaged, holed or rusty cans are rejected;

3 stock rotation is carried out.

Blown cans must not be used

The storage of perishable food

High-risk and perishable foods may be contaminated by harmful bacteria, which can multiply to dangerous levels if not stored under refrigeration.

The recent trend to remove additives means that some foods must now be stored under refrigeration when previously they did not need to be, e.g. opened bottles of tomato sauce.

Chilled storage

The common food poisoning organisms are incapable of multiplying and producing poisons at temperatures below 5°C. Furthermore, the spoilage of food by bacteria and mould is reduced. As can be seen from the 'ten main reasons for food poisoning' (page 3), temperature control is the single most important factor in preventing food poisoning. Therefore, it is essential for food handlers to receive clear instructions on the use of chillers/refrigerators to ensure that they operate effectively. In addition to the growth of food poisoning organisms, the major hazard, which may occur in chilled storage, is the contamination of high-risk food from raw food.

Controls

Include maintaining chillers at the correct temperature (alarmed units are recommended), separation of high-risk and raw foods, stock rotation, satisfactory storage containers/packaging and staff training on the correct use of refrigerators/chillers.

The correct use of refrigerators

Siting

Refrigerators should be sited in well-ventilated areas away from heat sources, such as ovens and the rays of the sun.

Construction

Refrigerators should be constructed to facilitate easy cleaning. Internal linings and shelves should be impervious and non-corroding. Door seals must be maintained in good condition and the unit should be serviced regularly.

Operating temperature

Units should normally operate between 1°C and 4°C. A thermometer should be permanently positioned in the warmest part of the refrigerator and the temperature checked and recorded, preferably three times a day.

Defrosting and cleaning

Defrosting and cleaning should be carried out in accordance with the manufacturer's instructions. Most units defrost automatically and should be cleaned and disinfected at least weekly. Bicarbonate of soda (one tablespoon to a gallon of water) may be used, but perfumed cleaning agents must not.

Packing and stock rotation

Refrigerators must not be overloaded, and food should never be placed in front of cooling units. Space should be left between products for air circulation. Only perishable foods should be stored in the refrigerator. This includes vacuum packs and pasteurised cans of meat. Stock rotation is essential to avoid spoilage.

Refrigerators must not be overloaded

Hot food

Hot food must never be placed directly into a refrigerator if this would raise the temperature of food already being stored above 5°C. It will also encourage condensation and consequently contamination. Joints of meat intended to be eaten cold should be kept below 2.25kg (5lbs) and less than 5cm thick to facilitate cooling prior to refrigeration.

Contamination and covering of food

Raw food must always be kept apart from high-risk food. Separate refrigerators are preferred, although, if in the same unit, the raw food must always be placed at the bottom to avoid contamination. Food should be covered to prevent drying out, cross-contamination and absorption of odour. Care should be taken to protect foods such as lettuce, tomatoes and cucumbers from dripping blood.

Open cans of food

Opened and part-used cans of food, especially acid food such as fruit, fruit juice or tomatoes, must not be left in the can as this may result in chemical contamination. The unused contents should be emptied into a suitable container, such as a plastic bowl, covered and placed in the refrigerator.

Staff training and responsibilities

All food handlers must receive instruction on the correct use of the refrigerator especially in relation to contamination and temperature control. They should be told not to keep the door open for longer than necessary. The temperature of refrigerated deliveries should be checked on arrival.

Freezers and frozen food

Commercial freezers should operate at -18°C or slightly below. At this temperature food will keep for a reasonable time with no bacterial growth. However, spores and dormant pathogens will survive and if the temperature rises above -10°C, spoilage organisms, especially moulds and yeast, begin to cause problems. Other hazards include contamination and freezer burn (dehydration).

Controls

Staff must be trained to use freezers and handle frozen food correctly. The temperature, and packaging, of deliveries of frozen food should be checked before unloading. If the temperature is around -18°C the food should be transferred to the freezer as quickly as possible (alarmed units are recommended). Deliveries above -15°C should be rejected and management advised. New stock should always be placed below existing food. Food must not be stored above the freezer load line and must not be kept for longer than recommended by the manufacturer, as the quality gradually deteriorates. Suitable packaging is essential to avoid freezer burn. Raw food and high-risk food should be separated.

A general guide for food kept at -18°C is:	
	Months
vegetables, fruit, most meat	up to 12
pork, sausages, offal, fish, butter and soft cheese	up to 6

Thawing of frozen food

Most food taken from the freezer can be cooked immediately, but poultry and large joints must be completely thawed before cooking. The manufacturer's instructions should always be followed. Thawing of raw meat/poultry must take place in an area entirely separate from other foods, which may be exposed to contamination hazards from thawed liquid. This area must never be used for cooked food, which is cooling prior to refrigeration. Thawing is best carried out at 10°C to 15°C or in a thawing cabinet. Sufficient time must always be allowed for thawing.

Thawing can also be achieved using clean, cold running water, below 15°C, or in an appropriate microwave oven, although extreme care is necessary because of the risk of uneven heating.

Thawing times in refrigerators vary considerably depending on the temperature, e.g. a 1.1 Kg bird takes around 70 hours at 1°C, 40 hours at 5°C and 13 hours at 10°C to reach 0°C.

Before using a refrigerator for thawing, it is essential to know the temperature of the refrigerator and the time a specific frozen chicken or other food product takes to thaw at that temperature. Extreme care must also be exercised to avoid cross-contamination. A refrigerator operating at 10°C and used solely for thawing food may be a cost effective solution.

Once completely thawed, food must be immediately refrigerated or cooked to avoid bacteria multiplying after thawing. Areas used for thawing should be thoroughly cleaned and disinfected.

Frozen food must not be thawed near high-risk foods

Rules for handling frozen poultry:

1 keep separate from other foods;

2 thaw completely in a cool room. Poultry will be ready for cooking when the body is pliable, the legs are flexible and the body cavity is free from ice crystals;

3 remove giblets;

4 once thawed, keep in the refrigerator and cook within 24 hours;

5 cook thoroughly and cook the stuffing separately;

6 all utensils and surfaces used for the preparation of raw meat and poultry must be thoroughly cleaned and disinfected before being used for high-risk food;

7 eat straight after cooking or, if the bird is to be carved cold, cool it quickly and store in the refrigerator. As with all meats refrigerated storage is essential within 1.5 hours;

8 avoid handling the cooked bird.

Thawing and cooking times of frozen poultry	Oven ready weight Kg (lbs)	Approximate thawing time at room temperature hours	Minimum cooking time at 180°C/350°F Gas 4 (in foil) hours
	2.25 (5)	15	2.5
	4.50 (10)	18	3.5
	6.75 (15)	24	4.75
	9.00 (20)	30	5.75

These are minimum times. The bird is cooked when the juices run clear from the thickest part of the bird (usually the deep thigh meat).

Stock rotation

Satisfactory rotation of stock, to ensure that older food is used first, is essential to avoid spoilage and ensure food is of good quality and safe. Most food must be labelled 'use-by' for high-risk foods with short shelf-life or 'best-before' for foods with longer shelf-life. Details of any special storage conditions, for example, keep below 3°C, should also be included. Daily checks should be made on short-life perishable food stored in refrigerators, whereas weekly examination of other foods may suffice.

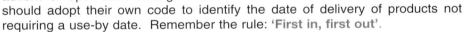

Stock which is undisturbed for long periods will encourage rodent and insect infestations. Good stock rotation has the added advantage of assisting in the maintenance of the correct levels of stock.

Stock rotation has been much easier since the advent of open-date coding. Food handlers should adopt their own code to identify the date of delivery of products not requiring a use-by date. Remember the rule: **'First in, first out'**.

Food preparation

The main hazards likely to occur during preparation are cross-contamination and the multiplication of bacteria. The observance of good hygiene practices during food preparation is an essential element in preventing food poisoning. Raw food and high-risk food should be prepared in different areas with separate, clean equipment. Raw food should be washed thoroughly in a separate sink, which is not used for washing utensils etc. and is positioned to avoid cross-contamination of high-risk food or clean utensils/equipment. Disposable wiping cloths should be used.

The handling of food should be minimised and it must not be left in a warm, humid atmosphere. The minimum amount of food should be prepared and then returned to refrigeration. Many schools and hospitals prepare food just prior to consumption, as required, as an additional safeguard. Food handlers should work in a logical, planned manner ensuring that working surfaces are kept as tidy as possible. Spillages and waste food should be cleared away promptly. Once again, staff training is essential.

Cooking/processing

Inadequate cooking enables pathogenic bacteria to survive and is a serious hazard. Furthermore, prolonged cooking at low temperatures, e.g. large rolled joints, allows bacteria at the centre to multiply to large numbers which may not be destroyed if satisfactory final centre temperatures are not achieved. Contamination can occur, for example, by repeat tasting with the same unwashed spoon, or physical contamination from condensation, flaking paint or insects if uncovered cooking pans are used. Chemical contamination may also occur if acid food, such as fruit, is boiled for prolonged periods in cooking utensils made from inappropriate materials, such as copper or aluminium.

As some food poisoning bacteria can produce toxins, which will withstand boiling for over 30 minutes, and spores may survive temperatures in excess of 100°C, cooking in isolation cannot be relied on to guarantee safe food. Effective storage is necessary to prevent toxin production prior to cooking. Immediately after cooking, food should be eaten as soon as possible or cooled rapidly to prevent the multiplication of bacteria from spores which are activated as a result of cooking.

Controls

Food must be cooked for the time and temperature recommended by the manufacturer. As a general guideline, a centre temperature of at least 75°C is recommended for raw, frozen and chilled food, and this should be checked with a disinfected probe thermometer. Food being reheated for immediate consumption should be heated to at least 82°C and this is a legal requirement in Scotland. Any unused reheated food should be discarded. Frozen joints and poultry must be completely thawed before cooking, and stuffing should be cooked separately. The base of pans should not exceed the heat source and stews and sauces should be stirred frequently. Pans should always be covered when not stirring to avoid contamination.

Only a clean, disinfected spoon should be used for tasting, and food handlers should be trained in effective cooking techniques, preventing contamination and the use of probe thermometers.

Processed food, such as canned vegetables and meat, receives temperatures of at least 121°C for three minutes, or the equivalent, to destroy spore-forming bacteria. As the temperature within ovens and retorts may vary, it is advisable to undertake cooking trials to establish the coldest spot in the appliance and the most effective way of cooking.

Microwave cooking

Microwave ovens are a safe and effective method of cooking and heating food, provided that manufacturer's instructions are followed. The destruction of food poisoning organisms is based on a combination of high temperatures and sufficient time and it is essential to know the power (wattage) of the oven and to allow adequate time to achieve the temperatures to ensure the safety of the food. Food should usually be heated throughout to at least 75°C and this should be checked in several places, using a probe thermometer, to guard against the possibility of cold spots. Stirring of liquids may be required and standing time may also be necessary on completion of cooking. Domestic microwave ovens are unsuitable for commercial operations.

Cooling

The hazards associated with cooling include the growth of food poisoning bacteria not destroyed during cooking, the production of toxins, the germination of spores and the contamination of food by micro-organisms, foreign bodies or chemicals.

The time between: refrigeration and cooking (or processing); cooking and refrigeration; refrigeration and serving; must be kept as short as possible.

Food must not be left in the danger zone of temperature

Controls

Cooling of food should be undertaken as quickly as possible after cooking. Cooling trials, using a disinfected probe thermometer, will assist in determining the most effective way of cooling food. The maximum time recommended is 1.5 to 2 hours. However, this is often difficult to achieve without a blast chiller. Joints of meat can often take several hours to cool from 60°C to 10°C even in a chiller operating at 10°C. Cooling times can be reduced by minimising the weight and thickness of joints. A maximum weight of 6 lbs (2.5 kg) is recommended. Joints can be sliced after cooking, although it is essential that knives are thoroughly cleaned and disinfected and contamination from food handlers is not introduced. Iced water may be used to speed up cooling.

Stews and sauces can be decanted into clean and disinfected shallow containers. Rice can be cooled using cold running potable water. Bagged joints can be sprayed with cold water. Hot food should not be placed in a small refrigerator because the temperature of other foods may be raised and condensation is likely. However, once food has cooled for 1.5 hours, it may be placed in a large walk-in chiller, if the air temperature of the chiller is unaffected and there is no risk of contamination.

During cooling, food should be covered and completely separate from raw food. Food handlers need training in effective cooling techniques, preventing contamination and good personal hygiene. As soon as food has been cooled it should be stored below 5°C.

Serving

The hazards associated with serving food include the multiplication of food poisoning bacteria because of prolonged periods at ambient temperature and contamination from food handlers, equipment, utensils and price tags (retail). Self-service, of open food and buffets in particular, presents many potential hazards, from customers, which are difficult to control.

Controls

Refrigerated buffets and retail display units are recommended. However, where these are not provided, the minimum amount of food should be displayed. The maximum time recommended between cooking and serving or refrigeration and serving is 30 minutes, when the food is at ambient temperatures.

All equipment and utensils used for service must be maintained in good condition and effectively cleaned and disinfected, if they are likely to come into contact with food.

Serving utensils must be stored properly, especially ice-cream scoops. Food placed on tables, such as bread rolls, must not be re-used. All plates and utensils must be clean and dry, and those parts likely to come into contact with high-risk food should not be handled. Cutlery and cups should be held by the handles. Condiments should be kept in clean containers, covered where necessary.

Customers should not be able to handle open food. Food should be pre-wrapped, covered or protected with sneeze screens. Counters in retail outlets should not be used for food storage or preparation. Price tags should not be stuck into food.

Raw food and high-risk food must be kept entirely separate, with separate serving counters, utensils and equipment and different food handlers. As far as practicable, high-risk foods, including different types of cooked meat, should also be kept separate within the same storage units, e.g. on their own individual dishes. (Major outbreaks of typhoid and *E.coli* O157 have been exacerbated from cross-contamination between cooked meats stored on the same platter and sliced with the same slicing machine.)

Food, which is kept hot prior to serving, should be maintained above 63°C to avoid the multiplication of bacteria, especially from spore formers. Contamination will be prevented if containers are suitably covered. Stews and sauces should be stirred regularly.

Slicing machines are a major potential hazard and the blade should be cleaned and disinfected throughout the day. If practicable, meat should be sliced in batches and the slicer cleaned and disinfected for different types of meat.

Food handlers should always wear appropriate clean protective clothing and they should be trained in relation to temperature control, good personal hygiene and preventing contamination. Staff should not handle money and high-risk foods. Hands should be thoroughly washed after handling money. Separate staff are preferred.

Food which causes food poisoning smells, looks and tastes normal

What controls are necessary to minimise hazards from suppliers?
Why is correct storage and stock rotation of food important?
What are the essential features of a dry-food store?
What are the important rules for the safe use of refrigerators?
What are the important rules for the storage of frozen food?
What are the hazards associated with the thawing of frozen poultry?
What are the main hazards and controls involved with the preparation, cooking, serving and cooling of food?

Food spoilage and preservation

Spoilage commences in food as soon as it is harvested, taken from the sea or slaughtered. Spoilage results from the action of bacteria, moulds and yeasts. Poor hygiene practices, including poor temperature control, inadequate or unsuitable packaging and rough handling, result in damage and accelerates spoilage, as does pest infestation.

Signs of spoilage include:

1. off odours;
2. discolouration;
3. slime/stickiness;
4. mould growth (whiskers);
5. changes in texture, e.g. dry or spongy;
6. unusual taste, e.g. sour;
7. the production of gas;
8. blown cans or packs.

Preservation is the treatment of food to prevent or delay spoilage and destroy or inhibit the growth of pathogenic organisms, which would render the food unfit. Often a combination of techniques is used, e.g. cooking followed by refrigeration, vacuum packaging and refrigeration or pasteurisation and refrigeration. The taste of food is usually changed by preservation. Food may be preserved by the use of:

1. high temperatures, pasteurisation, ultra-heat treatment, sterilisation, cooking, canning and bottling;
2. low temperatures, refrigeration and freezing;
3. dehydration (the removal of moisture) e.g. soups, vegetables and meat;
4. chemicals e.g. salt, sugar, and sulphur dioxide;
5. vacuum packing (sous vide) and controlled atmospheres, e.g. meat and fish;
6. acid fermentation e.g. yoghurt, cheese, salami and pepperoni;
7. irradiation e.g. spices;
8. smoking of fish and meat, hot smoking(treat as high-risk), cold smoking(treat as raw).

Packaging is very important to extend the life of preserved foods, e.g. cans, tetrapacks, bottles and pouches. Once opened, the food should be treated as fresh and stored under refrigeration.

What are the main signs of food spoilage?
What are the main ways of preserving food?

Personal hygiene

Most people carry some type of food poisoning organism at one time or another, especially when they have diarrhoea and/or vomiting. Food handlers have a moral and legal responsibility to observe high standards of personal hygiene to ensure that they do not contaminate food.

Because our body temperature is 37°C, it is ideal for the growth of most food poisoning organisms, either in the intestines (e.g. *Clostridium perfringens*) or on our skin (e.g. *Staphylococcus aureus*). Food handlers should keep themselves scrupulously clean and a daily shower is recommended.

Food handlers are potentially the most serious hazard in a food business. Bad practices of food handlers may result in the contamination of high-risk food with food poisoning organisms. Furthermore, food handlers are responsible for a significant number of foreign body hazards. Staff must be aware of these potential hazards and how they can be controlled, especially by good hygiene practices.

Hands and skin

As the hands are in direct contact with food, they are the main routes for transferring food poisoning bacteria. Hands must be kept very clean at all times. The correct hand washing procedure is essential. A non-hand operated warm water spray is preferred. The hands should be wet and sufficient liquid soap applied to ensure a good lather. The fingertips, between the fingers, the hands, wrists and forearms should all receive attention. Where necessary, e.g. after visiting the toilet, a clean, soft bristled nailbrush should be used to brush and lather the fingertips and clean under the fingernails (a dirty nailbrush is a hazard). The hands should be rinsed thoroughly in warm running water (35°C to 45°C) to remove all the lather, bacteria and dirt.

Efficient drying of the hands with clean disposable paper towels is essential and will reduce the number of bacteria remaining. A paper towel may be used to turn off taps. Re-usable towels should not be used. Food handlers must wash their hands regularly throughout the working day and especially:

1 after visiting the toilet;
2 on entering the food room, after a break and before handling any food;
3 after putting on or changing a dressing;
4 after dealing with an ill customer;
5 after handling raw food, including eggs, and before handling ready-to-eat food;
6 after eating, smoking, coughing, sneezing or blowing the nose;
7 after combing or touching the hair, face, nose, mouth or ears;
8 after handling waste food or refuse;
9 after cleaning, or handling dirty cloths, crockery etc; and
10 after handling external packaging, flowers or money.

As fingernails may harbour bacteria, they must be kept short and clean. Nail varnish and false fingernails may contaminate food and should not be used. People who continually put their fingers in their mouth, e.g. nail biters, should not be employed as food handlers. Licking the fingers before picking up sheets of wrapping paper is a particularly bad habit.

The nose, mouth and ears

Up to 40 percent of adults carry staphylococci in the nose and mouth. Coughs and sneezes can carry droplet infection for a considerable distance and persons with bad colds should not handle open food. Disposable single-use paper tissues are preferable to handkerchiefs. Picking or scratching the nose is not acceptable. Sleeves should never be used for wiping the nose.

As the mouth is likely to harbour staphylococci, food handlers should not eat sweets, chew gum, taste food with a finger or an unwashed spoon or blow into glasses to polish them. Apart from being aesthetically unacceptable, spitting can obviously result in food contamination and is illegal.

Discharges from the ears, eyes and nose may contaminate food and employees must report these ailments to their supervisor. Medical clearance to start work will normally be required.

Cuts, boils, whitlows and septic spots

Cuts, spots and sores provide an ideal place for bacterial multiplication. To prevent contamination of food by harmful bacteria and blood, these lesions should be completely covered by waterproof dressings, preferably coloured blue or green to aid detection if they become detached. Dressings should be replaced immediately they become loose. Cuts on fingers may need the extra protection of waterproof fingerstalls. Waterproof dressings will also assist in preventing cuts going septic. Some plasters contain a metal strip so that if they fall off they can be removed by a metal detection system.

Food handlers with colds, boils and septic cuts must not handle food

Jewellery and perfume

Food handlers should not wear earrings, watches, jewelled rings or brooches, as they harbour dirt and bacteria. Furthermore, stones and small pieces of metal may end up in the food and result in a customer complaint.

Food handlers should not wear strong-smelling perfume or aftershave, as it may taint foods, especially those with a high fat content.

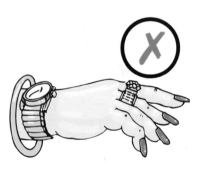

The hair

Hair is constantly falling out and, along with dandruff, can result in contamination of food. Furthermore, the scalp often contains harmful bacteria and must be shampooed regularly. Food handlers should wear suitable head covering which completely encloses the hair. Hairnets worn under turbans, helmets and hats are recommended and should always be put on before protective clothing. Combing of hair and adjustments to head covering should only take place in cloakrooms and should not be carried out whilst wearing protective clothing, as hairs may end up on the shoulders and then in the product.

Smoking

It is illegal to expose food to risk of contamination by smoking in food rooms or whilst handling open food. Not only is this to prevent cigarette ends and ash contaminating food but also because:

1. people touch their lips whilst smoking and they may transfer harmful bacteria to food;
2. smoking encourages coughing and droplet infection;
3. cigarette ends contaminated with saliva are placed on working surfaces;
4. an unpleasant environment may be created for non-smokers.

Protective clothing

Food handlers must wear clean and washable over-clothing, preferably light-coloured without external pockets. Press-studs or velcro fastening are preferable to buttons. Protective garments should be appropriate for the work being carried out and should completely cover ordinary clothing. Jumper and shirtsleeves must not protrude and, if short-sleeved overalls are worn, only clean forearms must be visible. Suitable footwear should be worn to prevent slipping and to protect the feet.

Staff must be aware that protective clothing is worn to protect the food from risk of contamination and not to keep their own clothes clean. Dust, pet hairs and woollen fibres are just a few of the contaminants carried on ordinary clothing. Protective clothing should not be worn outside the food premises, not used to travel to and from work and not worn during lunchtime sporting activities such as

football. Food handlers handling high-risk foods should remove their protective clothing when eating in staff canteens used by food handlers involved with raw food preparation. Segregation of workers in canteens is recommended, if separate facilities are not provided.

Outdoor clothing and personal effects must not be brought into food rooms unless stored in suitable lockers. Protective clothing should not be hung in sanitary accommodation.

Hands should not be wiped on protective clothing, especially after handling raw meat or poultry. Protective clothing should be removed when visiting the toilet. This is particularly important for food handlers involved with high-risk food preparation. Even when wearing protective clothing, food handlers should not sit on preparation surfaces.

General health and reporting of illness

Food handlers should be in good health in all aspects from oral hygiene to general fitness. Any food handlers suffering from diarrhoea, vomiting or a food-borne infection must not handle food. They must notify their supervisor who must exclude them from any work which would expose food to risks from pathogens. Food handlers who have consumed a meal known to have caused food poisoning or live in the same household as a confirmed case or have suffered from diarrhoea or vomiting whilst abroad should also report to the supervisor who will probably require them to visit the doctor. The doctor should be advised when a patient is a food handler. Food handlers who excrete food poisoning organisms or with skin infections, infected cuts, boils, heavy colds and ear or eye discharge must be excluded and should not resume food-handling duties without clearance. Even a boil on the leg may result in a hazard if, for example, a dressing is changed and hands are not washed properly.

Hygiene training

All food handlers must receive the appropriate supervision and instruction and/or hygiene training commensurate with their work activities. This will ensure that they are aware of the hygiene hazards associated with their job and the controls necessary to ensure the safety of food produced. A training programme should be implemented to ensure the competency (skill and knowledge) of all food handlers to produce safe food. Programmes should include induction training, hygiene awareness instruction, attending appropriate courses, practice and implementation and refresher training. Training involves more than attending courses and certification does not guarantee competency.

Why is personal hygiene important in preventing food poisoning?
When must food handlers wash their hands?
How can food handlers contaminate food?
When should food handlers report illness to their supervisor?
What are the important properties of protective clothing?

The construction and design of food premises

Site selection

The selection of a suitable site is most important when planning food premises. Consideration must be given to the provision and availability of services, i.e. electricity, gas, water supply and effluent disposal and the accessibility for deliveries and refuse collection. The possibility of flooding and pollution must also be considered.

Design of food premises

The satisfactory design and maintenance of food premises is essential to avoid hazards of contamination and the multiplication of bacteria. The food preparation and storage areas must be large enough to site all essential equipment, enable the effective separation of raw and high-risk food and permit satisfactory workflows for food, food handlers, 'dirties' and waste. Premises must be kept clean and in good repair and condition. Raw food preparation areas and high-risk preparation areas should be provided with separate equipment and have separate facilities for securing personal hygiene and washing equipment and utensils.

Food handlers are more likely to wash their hands before handling food if the wash-hand basin is sited at the entrance to the food room. Refrigerators are more likely to be used if they are close to preparation areas.

After obtaining planning permission, the following design principles should be followed:

1. cross-contamination should be eliminated; clean and dirty processes and raw and high-risk food preparation must be separated. Work areas should be colour coded. A separate area for deboxing should be provided;
2. workflow should be continuous and progress in a uniform direction from raw material to finished product;

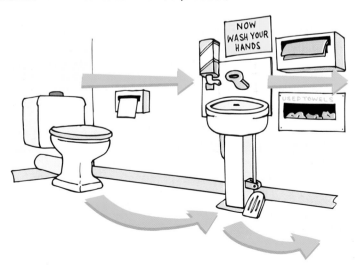

NOW WASH YOUR HANDS

USED TOWELS

The only way from a WC must be via a wash-hand basin

3 suitable and sufficient facilities for personal hygiene, cleaning and disinfecting equipment and washing food must be provided, together with adequate supplies of hot water and clean, wholesome cold water. Hot water should be around 60°C, cold water less than 10°C and warm water from spray taps around 35°C-45°C. Wash-hand basins should be positioned close to workstations and at the entrance of large rooms. The facilities should relate to working areas and process risks;

4 washing-up areas should be located away from high-risk food areas;

5 food should not be kept at ambient temperatures for longer than is absolutely necessary. Adequate conveniently located refrigeration to cater for peak demand is essential to avoid the multiplication of bacteria;

6 adequate cooking and cooling facilities must be provided. Flexible gas pipes should be used to allow movement of equipment for cleaning. Electrical supplies should be fitted with accessible cut-out switches. Trailing wires must be avoided. Waterproof sockets are preferred;

7 insects, rodents and birds must be denied access and harbourage;

8 suitable staff facilities must be provided including appropriate sanitary conveniences, separated from food rooms by ventilated spaces. Public sanitary accommodation must be provided in restaurants, cafés and public houses;

9 adequate drainage capable of removing peak loads quickly without flooding must be provided;

10 suitable and sufficient ventilation is necessary to ensure reasonable working conditions and reduce temperatures and humidities. Steam and heat-producing appliances require suitable canopies;

11 high standards of lighting are necessary to facilitate cleaning and provide safe and satisfactory working conditions. Lighting systems should not produce shadows or glare, and fluorescent tubes should be protected by diffusers;

12 premises should be designed to avoid the accumulation of dirt in inaccessible places and the risk of contamination from condensation. They must be capable of being thoroughly cleaned and disinfected;

13 all food premises must have a satisfactory, constant supply of potable (drinking) water.

Construction details

Ceilings

Ceilings should be smooth, fire-resistant, non-flaking, light-coloured, coved at wall joints and easy to clean. They should also reduce condensation.

Wall finishes

Finishes should be smooth, impervious, non-flaking, durable, light-coloured and capable of being thoroughly cleaned and, where necessary, disinfected. Surfaces may need to be resistant to spillages, chemicals, grease, heat and impact. Internal walls should be solid, as cavities provide harbourage for pests.

The correct design and construction of premises is essential for good hygiene

Floor surfaces

Surfaces should be durable, non-absorbent, anti-slip, without crevices and capable of being effectively cleaned. They may need to be resistant to acids, grease and salts, and, where necessary, should slope sufficiently for liquids to drain to trapped gullies. The angle between walls and floors should be coved.

Windows and doors

Windows, if present, should be fixed on north-facing walls to reduce glare and solar heat gain. If there is a risk of infestation, opening windows must be fitted with cleansable fly-screens. Where appropriate, external doors should be screened and all doors should be self-closing.

Wooden finishes

Wood should not normally be used but if unavoidable, e.g. window frames, it should be well-seasoned, properly knotted, stopped and primed and given three coats of polyurethane paint.

The storage and disposal of waste

Suitable receptacles should be provided, both inside and outside food premises, for the disposal of waste food and debris. Disposable polythene sacks or plastic bins are usually provided for internal use and dustbins or skips for external use.

Refuse containers used internally must be emptied as frequently as necessary and always at the end of the day. Polythene sacks should be tied securely when full and placed in the external waste receptacle. Foot-operated bins are recommended. After emptying, reusable containers must be thoroughly cleaned before being brought back into the food room. Waste-disposal units are commonly used for removing food debris.

Receptacles used for storage or collection of refuse should not be reused for the storage of food. Empty food containers, which are intended for reuse, e.g. bottles and trays, must be protected from contamination, especially by dogs. It is preferable to store such containers in a suitable room or well clear of the floor under a lean-to.

External refuse areas must be kept clean and tidy so as not to attract rodents, birds and insects. Dustbins must have tight-fitting lids and should never overflow. Compactors, which completely enclose the refuse, are preferred. Receptacles must be emptied as frequently as necessary and the yard surface must be hosed down regularly to avoid creating a nuisance. After emptying, waste receptacles should be rinsed out. Hands must always be washed after emptying refuse containers and handling waste.

Trade waste agreements should be made with the Local Authority or a reputable company.

How can the correct design of food premises prevent cross-contamination?
What facilities are required for personal hygiene and for cleaning food and equipment?
Why must food premises be well constructed and kept in good repair?
What provision must be made for the safe disposal of waste?
What provision should be made for effective temperature control?

Equipment for food handling

All equipment, working surfaces and other utensils which are used in food premises should be designed and constructed to minimise harbourage of soils, bacteria or pests, and to enable them to be thoroughly cleaned and disinfected. Surfaces in contact with food should be smooth, impervious, non-toxic, non-flaking, corrosion-resistant, durable and suitable for their intended use. Resistance to heat and attack by milk and acid foods, such as fruit juices, may need to be considered. Cracked, chipped, broken and badly-pitted equipment harbours dirt and bacteria, and should not be used.

Equipment which cannot be, or is not, effectively cleaned is hazardous. Equipment, which is made from inappropriate materials, damaged, worn or badly designed, may result in physical contamination of food. Furthermore, equipment which is not used properly may transfer bacteria to high-risk food, e.g. if the same equipment is used for raw food and high-risk food.

Food-grade stainless steel is appropriate for most equipment. Soft wooden surfaces should not be used, as they are absorbent,

Wooden, dirty and defective equipment must not be used

incapable of being cleaned and disinfected and may splinter. Cutting boards and handles of knives and brushes may be made from polypropylene or other suitable synthetic material. Tubular stainless steel is preferred to painted or galvanised angle iron.

The use of different colours or shapes as a code to ensure equipment used for raw food is not used for high-risk food is recommended. Red is usually used for raw food, blue for cooked food and green for salad vegetables.

Where practicable, and with due regard to safety, equipment should be mobile to facilitate its removal for cleaning. This is particularly important if sited close to walls. All guards must be capable of being thoroughly cleaned.

Equipment must be kept clean

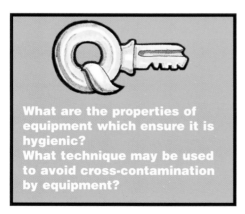

What are the properties of equipment which ensure it is hygienic?
What technique may be used to avoid cross-contamination by equipment?

Pest recognition and control

A **food pest** is an animal, which lives in or on man's food and is destructive, noxious or troublesome. Food pests, including dogs, cats and other pets, are a source of food poisoning organisms and a major hazard for food businesses. Pests may contaminate food with hair, fur, droppings, eggs and dead bodies. Flies vomit on food during feeding and may have just left a pile of refuse or animal faeces before visiting a food premises. Rats and cockroaches live in sewers and amongst rubbish and accumulations of rotting debris.

Food premises attract pests because they provide the ideal habitat. Most premises provide food, warmth, harbourage and moisture (condensation). Raw materials, including packaging, may bring pests into the premises and susceptible products should be carefully checked before transferring to storage. The common pests found in the food industry include:

1. rodents: rats and mice;
2. insects: flies, wasps, moths, cockroaches, psocids (booklice), silverfish, stored product insects and ants;
3. birds: mainly feral pigeons, sparrows and starlings.
4. occasional problems from feral cats.

Reasons for control:

1. to prevent the spread of disease;
2. to prevent the contamination and wastage of food (from bodies, droppings and urine);
3. to prevent damage (fires caused by gnawing electric cables or flooding caused by gnawing of pipes);
4. to prevent loss of custom and profit (caused by selling contaminated food or because of the discomfort or fear of customers using public areas of a food premises which are infested with mice, cockroaches or wasps);
5. to avoid losing staff who will not wish to work in infested premises;
6. to comply with the law and to avoid being fined or closed.

General pest control

Pests require security, shelter and food. Denial of these environmental factors will prevent their survival and is the first line of defence against possible infestations. Environmental control may be considered as:

Denial of access by care in design, maintenance and proofing of buildings. Doors and windows should be kept closed or if left open should be screened with a fine, cleansable mesh. Doorways can be protected

"Mice gnawed through your electrics? Look what they did to my hose!"

RODENTS

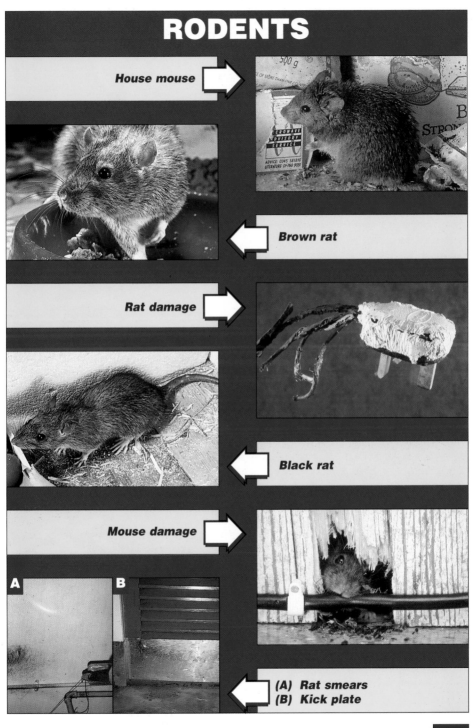

House mouse

Brown rat

Rat damage

Black rat

Mouse damage

(A) Rat smears
(B) Kick plate

A
B

COMMON FOOD PESTS

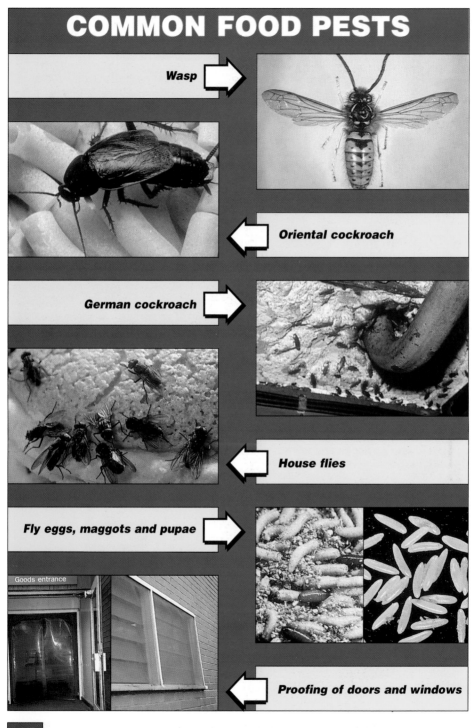

Wasp

Oriental cockroach

German cockroach

House flies

Fly eggs, maggots and pupae

Goods entrance

Proofing of doors and windows

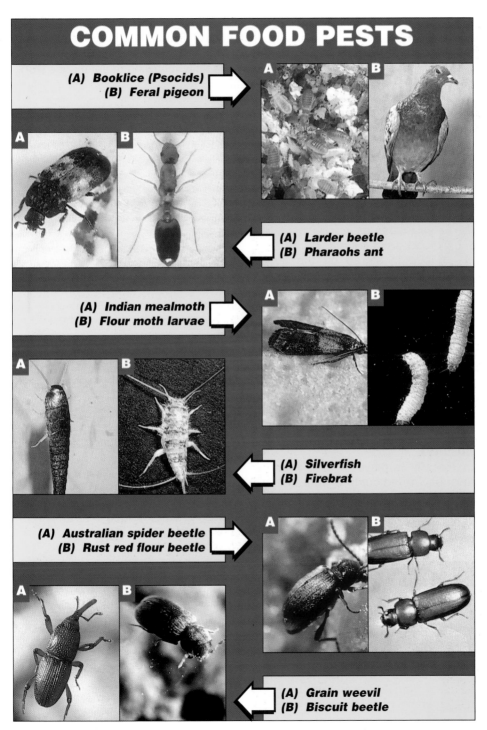

COMMON FOOD PESTS

(A) Booklice (Psocids)
(B) Feral pigeon

(A) Larder beetle
(B) Pharaohs ant

(A) Indian mealmoth
(B) Flour moth larvae

(A) Silverfish
(B) Firebrat

(A) Australian spider beetle
(B) Rust red flour beetle

(A) Grain weevil
(B) Biscuit beetle

Photograph courtesy of Rentokil Initial Limited

43

with hanging plastic strips or air curtains and the bottom of wooden doors should be protected with metal plates. Access holes and other openings should be sealed with mortar, metal sheets or mesh. Defects in buildings, such as broken windows or holes around pipes, especially following maintenance work, should be reported to management.

Denial of food and harbourage by good housekeeping.

Good housekeeping:

To reduce the risk of infestation it is important to prevent breeding and deny the lone invader the conditions it likes and in particular to ensure that:

1. premises and refuse areas are kept in a clean and tidy condition. Lids should be always kept on waste bins. After emptying, bins and the surrounding area should be hosed down. Waste must not be allowed to accumulate;
2. food on display or awaiting preparation is always kept covered;
3. you 'clean as you go' and clear away spillages promptly;
4. food is not left outside;
5. food is stored off the floor and clear of walls to facilitate regular inspection. Stock is checked regularly and damaged or contaminated stock removed and destroyed;
6. food is stored in pest-proof containers and lids are always replaced;
7. all deliveries of raw materials, packaging and laundry are checked to ensure their freedom from infestation;
8. drains are kept clean and in good condition. Taps are well maintained (i.e. no drips) and gullies have tight-fitting metal covers;
9. vegetation and other cover in the immediate vicinity of the food premises are removed;
10. regular inspections are made and sightings of pests or pest damage are reported to management immediately.

Surveys

Regular surveys of food premises must be carried out to ensure that they are pest free. In particular, food storage rooms, behind equipment, dark, undisturbed and waste storage areas should be examined. Signs to look for include:

Regular surveys are essential

1. live or dead bodies, including larvae, eggs and pupae from insects;
2. droppings, or webbing from moths;
3. damage, including gnawing marks in food, wood or plaster, holes in sacks, boxes, packets or in the structure, chewed pieces of cardboard or paper;

4 spillages adjacent to sacks of food (usually rodents);

5 scratching or gnawing sounds, e.g. in roof spaces (from rodents);

6 fur and nesting material;

7 unusual smells associated with mice and cockroaches in particular;

8 footprints and tail marks in dust or food powders such as flour;

9 rodent smears (black greasy marks) around pipes and holes and on walls adjacent to runways (usually rats);

10 the loss of small amounts of food (usually rodents).

Physical and chemical control

Although very important, environmental control may not be entirely successful and eradication must be achieved by using physical or chemical control methods.

Physical control methods are usually preferred as the pest is caught, either dead or alive, and consequently is not able to die in food, equipment or in some inaccessible place. Examples of physical control include ultra-violet, electric fly-killers, rodent traps and mist nets for birds. Sticky flypapers are unsightly but are useful in storage areas to alert you to flying insect problems.

Unfortunately, physical methods are not always successful and poisons have to be used. Rodenticides are used to kill rats and mice, and insecticides to kill insects. Care must always be exercised when using poisons to ensure there is no risk of contaminating food. Food and small utensils must always be removed when using insecticide, especially fly-sprays, and the premises and fixed equipment must be thoroughly cleaned after use. Infestations of food premises should be dealt with immediately and proprietors should seek assistance from the Local Authority or a specialist contractor. The control of cockroaches or stored product insects is particularly difficult and requires an expert pest control operator.

What is a food pest?
Why must pests be kept out of food premises?
What are the signs of an infestation of food pests?
How can pests be controlled in food premises?
How can pests be kept out of food premises?

Cleaning and disinfection

Effective cleaning and disinfection will remove microbiological hazards, however, unsatisfactory cleaning may result in the redistribution of contamination which may be an even greater hazard. Chemical hazards from inappropriate use or storage of chemicals, and physical hazards from inappropriate or defective cleaning equipment may also occur.

Soiling of surfaces and equipment is unavoidable in food businesses. It is essential that such residues are not allowed to accumulate to levels which expose food to risk of contamination. Removal of food residues, dirt and grease is the process of cleaning. The chemical used for cleaning is known as a detergent. Disinfection is the process of reducing micro-organisms to a safe level which will not cause premature spoilage. The chemical used is a disinfectant.

The reasons for cleaning:

1. to remove matter on which bacteria would grow, thus reducing the risk of food contamination, food poisoning and spoilage;
2. to allow disinfection of specific equipment and surfaces;
3. to remove materials which would encourage pest infestations;
4. to reduce the risk of foreign matter contamination;
5. to remove dirt and grease and ensure a pleasant and safe working environment;
6. to promote a favourable image to customers;
7. to comply with the law.

Energy in cleaning

Cleaning involves the application of energy to a surface, to remove dirt and grease. Energy is applied as:
- physical, e.g. scrubbing
- heat, e.g. hot water
- chemical, e.g. detergent.

Improving chemical energy and increasing heat will reduce the amount of physical energy required.

After cleaning, disinfectants are used to destroy bacteria that remain. Hot water, around 82°C, steam and bleach are the commonest disinfectants. However, disinfectants need time to work and an appropriate contact time is essential.

Hot water, chemicals and physical energy must be used to clean

Effective cleaning

To be effective, cleaning must be planned, organised and implemented in all areas of food premises. Cleaning schedules should be written which stipulate:

1. what is to be cleaned;
2. the amount and type of chemical and equipment to use;
3. who is to clean it;
4. when to clean it and the frequency of cleaning;
5. how to clean it (the method);
6. how much time is allowed for cleaning it;
7. the safety measures;
8. the person responsible for checking that it has been effectively cleaned.

Safe cleaning

Staff must be trained to 'clean as they go' and never clean from raw areas to high-risk areas with the same equipment. They must always have regard to the provision of health and safety. Suitable protective clothing must be worn and the chemical manufacturer's instructions must always be followed. Mixing of chemicals may produce dangerous gases and/or explosion. Open food must not be exposed to risk of contamination during cleaning. Chemicals must always be stored separate from food and should never be emptied into unmarked or food containers, especially bottles. To be effective, and avoid taint, chemicals must be diluted correctly.

After use, the cleaning equipment itself must be cleaned and dried. Brushes and mops should be hung off the floor in non-food rooms or cupboards. Cleaning equipment used in toilets must not be used in food rooms.

Cleaning must be planned

What to disinfect

Although food rooms and equipment need to be regularly and thoroughly cleaned, not everything requires disinfecting. Food and hand-contact surfaces and equipment, such as food containers, cutting boards, preparation surfaces, slicing machines, utensils, switches, touchpoints, handles on drawers and refrigerators, will need cleaning and disinfecting several times throughout the day and always following the use of raw food before high-risk food is prepared. Suitable contact time is essential to destroy bacteria.

Walls, floors, drains and equipment legs require regular and thorough cleaning and degreasing but, as they do not contact food, are unlikely to require disinfection unless there is a risk of food contamination. Ovens and similar devices, which use high temperatures to destroy bacteria, do not require disinfection, but the door handles may. Surfaces used for high-risk food preparation will need cleaning and disinfecting throughout the day, whereas floors in preparation areas may be cleaned daily and floors in dry storage areas weekly (provided spillages are removed immediately).

The cleaning procedure

Cleaning and disinfection may consist of six basic stages:

1. **pre-clean:** removing loose soil by sweeping, wiping or pre-rinsing (a disposable paper towel may be used);
2. **main clean:** loosening of the surface grease and dirt using hot water and a detergent. A brush or cloth will probably be used;
3. **rinse:** removal of loose dirt and detergent using clean hot water;
4. **disinfection:** destroying micro-organisms using heat or a chemical disinfectant and allowing sufficient contact time;
5. **final rinse:** removal of disinfectant using clean hot water (this is often unnecessary);
6. **drying:** preferably natural by evaporating dry.

Sanitisers, which combine a detergent and disinfectant, may be used on lightly-soiled surfaces, provided adequate contact time is allowed. (Stages 2 to 4 are combined.) In light-soil conditions the pre-clean may be combined with the main clean. Soiled or cooled water must be changed as frequently as necessary. If air-drying is not possible, single-use paper towels or a clean, dry cloth should be used. Hands should always be washed after cleaning before handling food.

Double-sink washing

Although the use of mechanical dishwashers and glasswashers is common, double-sink washing is recommended when suitable dishwashing machines are not available. The following procedure should be followed:

1. remove any heavy or loose soil by scraping and rinsing in cold water;
2. place articles in the first sink in detergent solution at 50°C to 60°C, scrub with a nylon brush and/or wipe with a clean cloth to loosen dirt residues. Rubber gloves will be required. Cool or dirty water should be replaced;
3. re-immerse in the first sink to wash off loosened dirt;
4. place articles in the second sink to rinse off chemical residues;
5. leave for 30 seconds at 82°C to achieve disinfection (alternatively a chemical disinfectant may be used at a lower temperature, e.g. around 60°C for 30 seconds);
6. remove the articles, allow to drain and air dry on a clean, disinfected surface. After drying, store in a clean place free from contamination.

Double-sink washing

Dishwashers are commonly used for cleaning and disinfecting. The wash cycle operates at around 60°C and the rinse cycle between 82°C and 88°C. The manufacturers' instructions must be followed and the right chemicals must be used. The sprayer arm jets must be clear of obstruction and the machine must be correctly stacked. Soiled utensils should be washed as soon as possible and clean utensils should be allowed to air dry.

Before cleaning electrical equipment, such as slicing machines, they must be switched off at the mains and isolated. Appropriate protective clothing must always be worn, e.g. rubber gloves, aprons, boots and goggles.

Why is it important to clean food premises and equipment regularly?

What is the difference between cleaning and disinfection?

What are the six basic stages in cleaning and disinfection?

Which surfaces should be disinfected?

The law relating to food and food safety

The law is a complex subject and most Acts and Regulations affecting the food industry are difficult to comprehend. However, ignorance of the law is no defence in the event of a prosecution, and all food handlers should make special efforts to understand the legislation that affects their business and themselves. This book contains only very brief details of some of this legislation and more information may be obtained from your local Environmental Health Officer.

Acts and Regulations applicable to the food industry are concerned with:

1. the production or sale of injurious, unsafe, unfit or substandard food;
2. the contamination of food;
3. the hygiene of food premises, equipment and personnel;
4. hazard analysis and hygiene practices, including temperature control and treatment;
5. the control of food poisoning and food-borne diseases;
6. the composition, volume, weight and labelling of food.

* Food Safety Act 1990

This is the most important Act relating to the sale of food for human consumption. It contains comprehensive provisions for securing food safety and empowers Ministers to make extensive hygiene regulations. The provisions of the Act are applicable to all food businesses in England, Scotland and Wales.

* In Northern Ireland, the Food Safety (Northern Ireland) Order, 1991 applies

It is an offence to render food injurious to health or to sell food which fails to comply with the food safety requirements by reason of it being injurious to health, unfit or so contaminated that it would be unreasonable to use it for human consumption.

An offence is also committed if food is sold which is not of the nature, substance or quality demanded by the purchaser. Legal action can be taken if food is falsely described or labelled.

Food which fails to comply with the food safety requirements, or which is likely to cause food poisoning, may be seized or detained by an authorised officer of a food authority. Expenses incurred in the destruction of food must be paid for by the owner. Compensation can be paid if the food is not condemned.

A person found guilty of the above offences may be liable to a fine of up to £20,000 and/or imprisonment for up to six months, although in serious cases unlimited fines and up to two years imprisonment may be incurred.

Failure to comply with food hygiene regulations may result in the service of an improvement notice specifying the contraventions, the measures necessary to secure compliance and the time allowed for compliance. Failure to comply with the improvement notice is an offence.

When an authorised officer is satisfied that there is an imminent risk of injury to health they may issue an emergency prohibition notice which requires the immediate closure of all or part of a food premises or the immediate prohibition of a process or use of equipment. An application must be made to the court for an emergency prohibition order within three days of serving the notice.

The court may also impose a prohibition on the proprietor or manager participating in the management of any food business.

It is a defence for a person to prove that they took all reasonable precautions and exercised all due diligence to avoid the commission of an offence by themselves or by a person under their control.

Insanitary premises can be closed

Due diligence

Due diligence is the principal defence under the Food Safety Act 1990 and enables a defendant to be acquitted of an offence if they prove that they 'took all reasonable precautions and exercised all due diligence to avoid committing the offence'. Taking reasonable precautions involves setting up a system of procedures and controls, having regard to the likely hazards and risks, and due diligence requires the systems to be operated properly. Written records are strongly recommended and could include reference to hazard analysis, specifications, training, temperatures, pest control, sampling, customer complaints, cleaning schedules and codes of practice.

Quality assurance and accreditation under ISO 9000 will be beneficial but will not guarantee the success of a due diligence defence. A written warranty from a supplier will be useful but is no longer an absolute defence.

It may be acceptable for a food operator to prove that someone else, not under their control, was responsible, that they were relying on information provided, that reasonable checks were made, there was no reason to suspect they were committing an offence and they could not reasonably know that an offence was being committed.

The Food Safety (General Food Hygiene) Regulations 1995

These Regulations control the hygiene standards of food premises other than those covered by their own specific regulations, such as dairies and slaughterhouses. The Regulations require the following.

1 Proprietors of food businesses must operate hygienically and
a) analyse food hazards that may arise in the food operation;
b) identify at which points in the operation these hazards may occur;
c) decide which of the points identified are critical to ensuring food safety (critical points);
d) implement effective control and monitoring procedures at these critical points and review these safety controls periodically and whenever food operations change.

2 Food premises must be kept clean and maintained in good repair and condition. They must be designed to permit good food hygiene practices, have adequate washbasins, flush lavatories and facilities for cleaning and disinfecting. Washbasins must be provided with hot and cold (or mixed) running water, soap and hygienic drying materials. Satisfactory standards of lighting and ventilation must be provided.

3 Walls, floors and food-contact surfaces of food rooms must be easy to clean and, where necessary, disinfect.

4 Conveyances and/or containers used for transporting foodstuffs must be kept clean and maintained in good repair and condition to protect foodstuffs from contamination.

5 Food equipment must be kept clean and in good repair and condition, to enable it to be kept clean and, where necessary, disinfected to minimise the risk of food contamination.

6 Food waste and refuse must not be allowed to accumulate in food rooms and adequate provision must be made for its storage in closed containers and its removal. It must be protected against pests.

7 An adequate supply of potable (drinking) water must be provided.

8 Food handlers must keep themselves clean and wear suitable clean and, where appropriate, protective clothing. If they know or suspect they are carrying a foodborne disease, or have an infected wound or skin condition, they must advise their manager and must not be permitted to work if they are likely to contaminate food with pathogens.

9 Food, including raw materials, must be fit for human consumption and stored and protected to minimise any risk of contamination.

10 Food handlers must be supervised and instructed and/or trained in food hygiene matters commensurate with their work activities.

11 Offences are punishable, on conviction, by a fine of up to £5,000 for each offence. In serious cases a sentence of up to two years imprisonment and unlimited fines may be imposed.

Food must not be exposed to risk of contamination

The Food Safety (General Food Hygiene) (Butchers' Shops) Amendment Regulations 2000

Butchers' shops and other retail outlets selling unwrapped raw meat and ready-to-eat food must be licensed annually. The fee is £100. Licence requirements include:

- Compliance with food safety legislation.
- A documented hazard analysis system, subject to verification.
- All food handlers to be satisfactorily trained in food safety.
- At least one person trained to enable him to supervise the food safety activities and the hazard analysis procedures.

Food Safety (Temperature Control) Regulations 1995

Food which needs to be kept chilled because it is likely to support the growth of pathogens or the formation of toxins must be kept at or below 8°C. Certain foods, e.g. raw food intended for cooking, are exempt, however, no food must be kept at a temperature which would result in a risk to health. (This may mean that some foods have to be stored below 8°C.) Limited periods outside temperature control, consistent with food safety, are permitted for preparation, transport, display and service, e.g. food displayed for less than four hours, on a single occasion.

Cooked food, which needs to be kept hot to prevent the growth of pathogens or the formation of toxins, must be kept at or above 63°C. Certain exemptions exist, e.g. food displayed for less than two hours. Where food has to be cooled it must be done as quickly as possible.

The Food Premises (Registration) Regulations 1991

These Regulations require food premises to register with their Local Authority at least 28 days before opening. Small bed and breakfast establishments, slaughterhouses and certain premises controlled by charitable organisations are included in the exemptions. A fine of up to £1,000 for failure to register or £5,000 for providing false information are the penalties for non-compliance.

Environmental Health Officers (EHOs)

Environmental Health Officers are authorised officers of the Local Authority who are empowered to enter (at any reasonable time) and inspect food premises, and close insanitary food premises. They will identify unsafe practices and investigate food complaints and incidents of foodborne illness. Improvement and Prohibition Notices may be issued, food seized or detained, records examined, samples and photographs taken and legal proceedings instituted for contraventions of legislation. Failure to co-operate may result in the offence of obstruction.

However, they are employed to protect the public and usually prefer to give written or verbal advice and offer guidance, especially at the planning stage. Do not hesitate to contact them if you need assistance.

What are the important acts and regulations relating to food safety and hygiene?
What action can be taken by a Local Authority to control the sale of unsafe, unfit, contaminated or substandard food?
What action can be taken if food premises are unhygienic or substandard?
What are the requirements of current legislation regarding premises, equipment, food handlers, washing facilities, services, practices and storage temperatures?
When can insanitary food premises be closed?

APPENDIX I
General rules for food handlers

1 Food handlers with skin, nose, throat or bowel trouble should inform their supervisor and must not handle food until medical clearance has been obtained.

2 Cuts, burns and sores must be covered with waterproof dressings. Persons with boils or septic cuts must not handle food. Fingernails must be kept clean and short, and nail varnish should not be used.

Food handlers who are ill must not handle food

3 All food handlers must wear suitable protective clothing and head covering. Outdoor clothing must not be brought into food rooms. Jewellery, hair grips and watches should be removed.

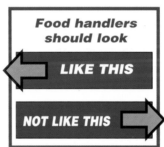

Food handlers should look

LIKE THIS

NOT LIKE THIS

4 Food handlers must not smoke in food rooms or whilst handling open food.

5 On entering a food room all food handlers should wash their hands. Hands must also be thoroughly washed after visiting the toilet, handling raw food, blowing the nose, handling refuse or swill, eating, smoking, cleaning and at frequent intervals during the work period.

Avoid sneezing over food

6 The mouth, nose or hair must not be touched during food preparation. Sneezing or coughing over food must be avoided.

7 All equipment, fixtures and fittings must be clean before preparation begins.

8   Raw food must always be kept separate from high-risk food at all stages of storage and preparation. Separate equipment, working surfaces and food handlers should be used to avoid cross-contamination from raw to high-risk food.

9   Frozen meat must be completely thawed before cooking. Thawing must be carried out separately from other processes. The liquid from thawing poultry etc. must not come into contact with other food, directly or indirectly, e.g. by use of a wiping cloth.

10   All meat must be cooked thoroughly. Rewarming cooked meats is potentially hazardous. All reheated foods, including meat, soup and gravy must be thoroughly reheated and consumed immediately.

11   If hot meat is not to be eaten immediately, it must be cooled quickly and placed in a refrigerator within 1.5 hours. High-risk food must be protected from contamination at all times and kept out of the danger zone of temperature, i.e. 5°C to 63°C.

12   Food must not be removed from the refrigerator until required for serving or preparation.

13   Display trolleys and buffets should be refrigerated and covered to prevent contamination.

14   Stored food must be rotated to prevent spoilage, avoid waste and prevent infestations. Out-of-date food and damaged canned or packaged food must not be sold.

15   Dirty pans, cutlery, crockery and other equipment should be cleaned and disinfected without undue delay.

16   If the use of drying cloths is unavoidable, they must be kept clean.

17   Dirty wiping cloths must not be used. Disposable cloths are preferred.

18   Spillages should be cleaned up promptly and food debris should not be allowed to accumulate.

19   Polythene sacks or suitable impervious containers, fitted with lids, should be used for the disposal of waste in food rooms.

20   Animals must not be allowed in food rooms. Infestations of insects or rodents must be reported immediately.

REMEMBER, YOUR CARELESSNESS MIGHT BE THE CAUSE OF AN OUTBREAK OF FOOD POISONING

Dirty food handlers will be prosecuted

APPENDIX II

The identification of steps critical to food safety (Hazard Analysis)

The Food Safety (General Food Hygiene) Regulations 1995 require proprietors of food businesses to identify any step in the activities of the food business which is critical to ensuring food safety and to ensure adequate safety controls are in place, maintained and reviewed.

Large food manufacturers with relatively few product lines may comply with this requirement by using a fully documented Hazard Analysis Critical Control Point (HACCP) System. An alternative approach to identifying and controlling steps critical to food safety will be more appropriate for other food businesses, especially catering and retailing, which have a large number of products often prepared simultaneously with a degree of flexibility inapplicable to manufacturing.

However, improvements in consistency and adherence to laid down procedures by catering and retailing businesses make the application of food safety management and the implementation of controls much more effective and enhance product safety.

To comply with the legislation, proprietors will need to examine their operation from purchase of raw materials to service of the customer on the basis of the following five principles.

Analysis of the food hazards associated with the food business operation

Hazards may be considered as:

1. Contamination of food by microorganisms (bacteria, toxins, moulds, viruses and parasites), chemicals (e.g. cleaning chemicals or pesticides) and physical (foreign bodies such as glass, pests or wire).

2. The growth of bacteria and moulds on or in food, usually due to storage at higher temperatures than recommended or being held at ambient temperatures for prolonged periods, i.e. several hours.

3. The survival of bacteria due, for example, to inadequate cooking or processing times and temperatures, failure to clean and disinfect in accordance with manufacturers' instructions or failure to add sufficient preservative.

Proprietors must decide which food hazards are likely to occur in their business. In particular, they should consider the bad practices that may result in food poisoning and the type of food complaints associated with their products.

Identification of the points in the operation where food hazards may occur

The following is an example of a simple flow diagram relating to some of the steps in a catering operation.

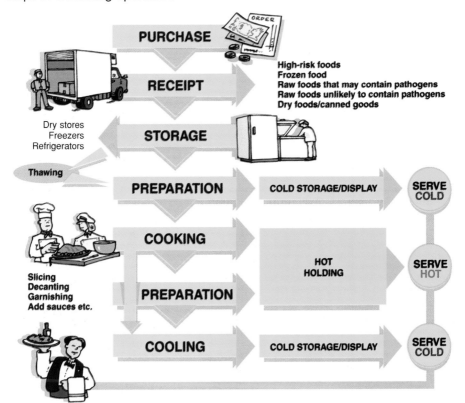

At each step microbiological contamination, physical contamination, bacterial multiplication (and survival) should be considered.

It will also be beneficial to consider personal hygiene, cleaning and disinfection, waste disposal and pest control generically, as they are relevant at each step.

Deciding which of the points identified are critical to ensuring food safety ('critical points')

At each step there are likely to be several hazards and the points at which the hazards must be controlled to ensure food safety should be considered as critical points. Bacterial contamination may occur during preparation of high-risk food, e.g. from unhygienic utensils or working surface, the hands of staff or raw food. Bacterial growth may occur if food is held at room temperature for too long.

The simple question to ask is 'could a failure to control the hazard at this step result in food poisoning or serious food complaint, e.g. shards of glass?' If the answer is 'yes', and the hazard will not be controlled at a later step, then the step is a critical point and the hazard must be controlled. If the answer is 'no', then good hygiene practice at the step should usually be sufficient to ensure food safety and to comply with the law.

Identification and implementation of effective control and monitoring procedures at the critical points

Controls must be implemented to eliminate the hazard or reduce it to a safe level. Measurable targets should be set and checks introduced to ensure targets are achieved. Temperature and times are two of the most important parameters as they are precise and relatively easy to monitor. For example, high-risk foods should be stored at or below 5°C and should not be left at ambient temperature for longer than 30 minutes. Personal hygiene controls are not as precise, although effective supervision should ensure instructions are adhered to, e.g. staff must wash their hands when entering the food room, after handling raw meat and at specific times during the day. Bacteriological cleanliness of equipment will require cleaning and disinfection of equipment at specific times in accordance with cleaning schedules.

Records are important for managers to confirm that the necessary monitoring has been undertaken. Written procedures on corrective action in event of targets not being met are also essential.

Controls need to be practical and capable of being carried out by the staff involved at the particular step. Additional instruction and training may be required.

Monitoring involves checking to ensure that controls are effective and are being implemented. The way in which controls are monitored will depend on the size and nature of the business. Examples of monitoring include:

- checking the temperature of refrigerators regularly and recording twice a day;
- checking that staff wash their hands on entering the food room;
- checking date codes to ensure satisfactory stock rotation; and
- checking that the core temperature of joints of meat reach at least 75°C.

When monitoring indicates a problem or a complaint is received then corrective action must be taken. For example, rejecting deliveries of out-of-date stock, increasing cooking times if correct centre temperatures are not achieved or adjusting the thermostat on the refrigerator if the storage temperature is too high. Corrective action will often involve issuing new instructions to staff and providing additional training. Staff and supervisors must be fully aware of the corrective action to take and it is preferable for these actions to be written down to avoid mistakes, especially when regular staff are on holiday or sick.

Review of the analysis of food hazards, critical points and the control and monitoring procedures periodically, and whenever the food business operations change

A review of the hazard analysis, control and monitoring systems will be necessary if:

1. controls are ineffective or the product is unsatisfactory;
2. the range or type of product alters, e.g. cooked chicken is purchased instead of raw;
3. the method of preparation changes, e.g. rice is boiled for immediate consumption instead of being cooled and reheated; and
4. new equipment is introduced, e.g. a microwave oven replaces a conventional oven.

Documentation of the system is not a legal requirement but effective documentation, which is implemented, will impress enforcement officers and commercial customers and assist a defence of due diligence in the event of prosecution. It is also extremely difficult to consistently apply controls and checks if there is no documentation. However, incomplete or falsified monitoring records are of little use.

Further information on hazard analysis may be obtained from:

1. your local Environmental Health Officer;
2. the Industry Guides to Good Hygiene Practice;
3. trade associations;
4. publications, videos and training aids from distributors of hygiene training aids.

A review of the Hazard Analysis system is necessary if controls are ineffective

Implementing hazard analysis

Control measures:
Actions required to eliminate or reduce hazards to a safe level.

Corrective actions:
The actions to be taken when the results of monitoring indicate a control point is moving out of control.

Critical control point (CCP):
A step in the process which must be controlled to eliminate or reduce a hazard to an acceptable level.

Critical limit:
The value of a monitored action which separates the acceptable from the unacceptable.

Hazard:
Something which may cause harm to the consumer. Hazards can be microbiological, physical or chemical.

Monitoring:
The observations and measurements at critical control points to confirm the process is under control.

Prior to the implementation of hazard analysis the premises should be designed and operated to minimise the risk of contamination and be well maintained. Equipment should be in good condition and subject to satisfactory maintenance agreements. Where necessary equipment must be calibrated, for example, thermometers.

It is also essential that the business operates in accordance with good hygiene practices. These practices are often omitted from the hazard analysis control chart but they remain important and must be monitored and corrective action taken if standards are unsatisfactory. Good hygiene practices include:

1. competent staff with high standards of personal hygiene;
2. effective cleaning and disinfection and the use of cleaning schedules;
3. effective pest management and electronic fly killers sited to prevent food contamination; and
4. effective waste management.

This approach will assist in reducing the number of critical control points to a manageable level and avoids spreading resources at critical control points too thinly.

AN EXAMPLE OF A HAZARD ANALYSIS
CONTROL CHART SHOWING STEPS IN THE OPERATION
CRITICAL TO FOOD SAFETY

Step	Hazard	Control	Monitoring	Corrective Action
Purchase of raw materials	Presence of contaminants; microbiological, chemical or physical.	Select least hazardous ingredients. Only use approved suppliers. Specification for product quality and safety including delivery temperatures. Food safety systems.	Inspect supplier or request records to show that they follow good manufacturing practice. Historical check of deliveries. Absence of customer complaints. Bacteriological sampling.	Revisit/inspect supplier. Change supplier. Review product specification.
Delivery of raw materials	Presence of contaminants. Multiplication of food poisoning bacteria.	Specify delivery requirements, especially time and temperature. Minimize time for unloading/placing in storage. Deboxing area. Food protected/covered.	Check delivery vehicles and drivers, date codes, time for unloading and temperature and condition of food (as per specification).	Refuse to accept delivery. Change supplier if it is a persistent problem. Review product specification.
Storage (chilled, frozen, dry)	Multiplication of food poisoning bacteria. Contamination due to poor hygiene practices.	Store at correct temperature (alarmed units). Cover/wrap food. Stock rotation/date codes. Separate raw/high-risk foods.	Check air/food temperature, date codes, and food complaint records. Audits and visual checks of food. Check condition of food and packaging.	Adjust temperatures. Repair/replace equipment. Use food immediately. Discard food. Review systems to prevent contamination.
Preparation	Multiplication of food poisoning bacteria. Contamination due to poor hygiene practices and poor personal hygiene.	Prepare minimum amount of food. Minimize time at room temperature. Separate raw/high-risk foods and use of separate equipment. Colour coding. Food protected/covered.	Check time/temperature. Audits/visual checks. Bacteriological swabbing of hands and surfaces.	Reduce time at ambient. Discard food. Review systems to prevent contamination.
Cooking/ baking/ heating (or reheating)	Survival of food poisoning bacteria. Contamination and multiplication also possible.	Centre temperature at least 75°C. (Reheat to 82°C). Ensure frozen poultry/joints completely thawed. Stir liquids. Protect from contamination. Cook just before eating.	Check time/temperature. Audits/visual checks.	Raise temperature. Increase time. Discard food. Repair/replace equipment.
Cooling	Multiplication of surviving food poisoning bacteria, or germination of spores. Contamination.	Minimise weight/thickness of joints. Cool rapidly (blast chiller). Cool in shallow trays. Keep covered. No contact with raw food. Refrigerate immediately after cooling.	Check time/temperature. Audits/visual checks.	Discard food. Repair/replace equipment (blast chiller). Review systems to prevent contamination.
Addition of fillings/ toppings	Contamination. Multiplication of food poisoning bacteria.	Use clean and disinfected equipment and work surfaces. Use separate equipment to avoid cross-contamination. Minimise time at ambient.	Audits/visual checks. Check time at ambient.	Discard food. Review systems to prevent contamination.
Service/ display	Contamination due to poor hygiene practices. Multiplication of food poisoning bacteria.	Minimise handling. Keep <5°C or >63°C. Keep food covered. Stock rotation. Separate raw/high-risk foods. Sell within shelf-life. Prevent customer contamination. Colour coding. Minimise time at room temperature.	Check time/temperature and date codes. Condition of food. Audits/ inspections.	Adjust temperatures/times. Discard food. Repair/replace equipment. Review systems to prevent contamination.

GLOSSARY

Additive	A chemical added to food, e.g. a preservative, a colouring or flavouring agent.
Aerobic	Using oxygen.
Anaerobic	Using little or no oxygen.
Antibiotic	A drug used to destroy pathogenic bacteria within human or animal bodies.
Antiseptic	A substance that prevents the growth of bacteria and moulds, specifically on or in the human body.
Bactericide	A substance which destroys bacteria.
Binary fission	A type of reproduction where the organism divides into two.
Carrier	A person who harbours, and may transmit, pathogenic organisms without showing signs of illness.
Cleaning	The removal of soil, food residues, dirt, grease and other objectionable matter.
Coliforms	Bacteria whose presence can indicate poor hygiene.
Contamination	The occurrence of any objectionable matter (including bacteria) in food or the food environment.
Cook-chill	A type of food production system where food is prepared, cooked, rapidly cooled and kept for a limited time period, under chilled storage prior to reheating.
Danger zone of bacterial growth	The temperature range within which multiplication of pathogenic bacteria is possible (from 5°C to 63°C).
Dehydrate	To remove water.
Detergent	A chemical used to remove grease, dirt and food particles.
Disinfection	The reduction of micro-organisms to a level that is safe and will not cause premature food spoilage.
E.C. directive	Legislation from the European Community that has to be included into member country laws.
Enzyme	A type of protein that speeds up a biological process and is unchanged by it.
First aid materials	Suitable and sufficient bandages and dressings, including waterproof dressings. All dressings to be individually wrapped.
Food business	Any business in the course of which commercial operations in respect of food or food sources are carried out (whether carried on for profit or not).
Food-borne disease	An illness resulting from the consumption of food (or water) contaminated by pathogenic micro-organisms (and/or toxins) which do not need to multiply within the food to cause illness.
Food hygiene	All measures necessary to ensure the safety and wholesomeness of food during preparation, processing, manufacture, storage, transportation, distribution, handling and offering for sale or supply to the consumer.
Food poisoning	An acute illness, usually with symptoms of diarrhoea and/or vomiting caused by the consumption of contaminated or poisonous food. (A multiplication of bacteria usually occurs

	within the food.)
Fungus	A parasitic or saprophytic plant lacking chlorophyll, which feeds by absorbing digested food through hyphae.
Gastroenteritis	An inflammation of the stomach and intestinal tract that normally results in diarrhoea.
Hazard	Something which may cause harm to the consumer (the safety aspect of the product) and can be microbiological, chemical or physical.
Immunity	The ability to resist an invading organism so that the body does not develop the disease.
Incubation (onset period)	The period between infection (or ingestion) and the first signs of illness.
Irradiation (of food)	The process of subjecting food to doses of ionising radiation, such as gamma rays, x-rays or electrons, to destroy parasites, insects and most micro organisms to extend the life of food and reduce the risk of food-borne illness.
Moulds	Microscopic plants (fungi) that may appear as woolly patches on food.
Optimum	Best.
Pasteurisation	A heat process used to reduce the number of micro-organisms to a safe level. Pasteurised food must be stored under refrigeration.
Pathogen	Disease-causing organism (harmful to humans).
pH	An index used as a measure of acidity/alkalinity
Protozoa	Single-celled organisms which form the basis of the food chain. Some are pathogenic e.g. cryptosporidium.
Residual insecticide	A long-lasting insecticide applied in such a way that it remains active for a considerable period of time.
Risk	The likelihood that the hazard will be realised.
Safe food	Food which is free of contaminants and will not cause illness or harm.
Sanitiser	A chemical agent used for cleansing and disinfecting surfaces and equipment.
Sous vide	An interrupted catering system, in which raw food is sealed in a vacuumised plastic pouch, cooked, rapidly chilled and reheated for service after a period of chilled storage.
Spore	A resistant resting phase of bacteria protecting them against adverse conditions such as high temperatures.
Steriliser	A chemical used to destroy all living organisms.
Sterile	Free from all living organisms.
Sterilisation	A process that destroys all living organisms.
Stock rotation	A control system which ensures that older stock is used first.
Toxins	Poisons produced by pathogens.
Viruses	Microscopic pathogens that multiply in the living cells of their host.
Water activity (a$_w$)	A measure of the available water in food.
Wholesome food	Sound food, fit for human consumption.
Zoonoses	Diseases which can pass from animal to man and vice versa.